Science

The Walls Belong to Kids

Thematic Classroom Activities & Bulletin Boards

by Anthony Flores and Jerry Dodge

Fearon Teacher Aids
Simon & Schuster Supplementary Education Group

Editors: Marilyn Trow and Sue Mogard
Copyeditor: Kristin Eclov
Design: Terry McGrath
Illustration: Tracy LaRue Hall
Cover Illustration: Tracy LaRue Hall
Cover Design: Marek-Janci Design

ISBN-0-86653-955-7

Printed in the United States of America

1. 9 8 7 6 5 4 3 2 1

(1995–96)

Contents

To the Teacher

The Walls Belong to Kids: Science is filled with bulletin-board projects that students and teachers work on cooperatively. The bulletin boards are designed to enhance any science curriculum. Bulletin boards are a very special part of elementary classrooms. They provide colorful and constant sources for review and study and may even become alternative assessments of student achievements. Bulletin boards many times reveal underlying understandings that are difficult to uncover with traditional paper and pencil tests.

Each bulletin-board project in this book contains four easy-to-follow steps:

Creating the Background: Materials and teacher procedures necessary to prepare the background for each bulletin board.

Exploring the Topic: Activities and discussions that invite students to discover connections between what students already know and the various science topics.

Applying Ideas: Challenges and guidance that help students work together to create bulletin boards that express their understandings of science issues.

Integrating Other Subject Areas: Additional opportunities that integrate science with other areas of the curriculum.

Bulletin boards created by and for students add more than artistic touches to classrooms. They become a very positive part of the classroom environment. Providing students with opportunities to participate in creating the environment in which they work will result in more learning and understanding. Create bulletin boards together!

Bulletin Boards

A Bouquet for Parents

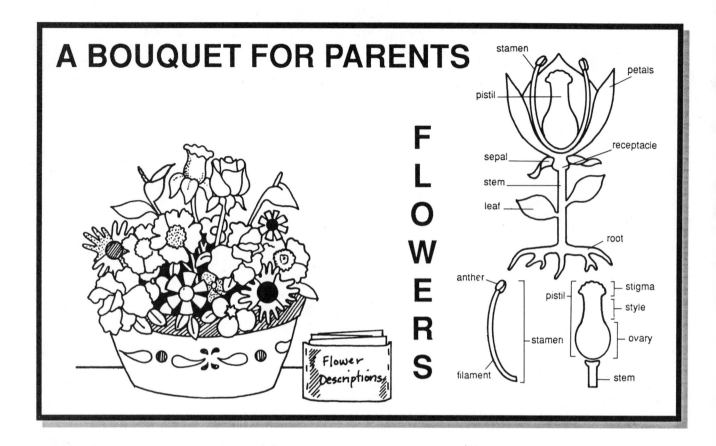

A BOUQUET FOR PARENTS

FLOWERS

stamen
petals
pistil
sepal
receptacle
stem
leaf
root
anther
pistil
stigma
style
stamen
ovary
filament
stem

Flower Descriptions

Flowers are intricately designed wonders of nature. Although they vary in color, size, and design, all flowers contain the same necessary parts that enable them to grow and reproduce. Each part is uniquely designed in size and shape to perform a specific function. Learning the plant parts common to all flowers will help students begin to see the many patterns present in nature. Students might enjoy creating this bulletin board for open house at school or during May and June to celebrate Mother's Day or Father's Day.

As students create this bulletin board together, they will:

- discover the different parts common to all flowers

- learn the names and functions of flower parts

- make flowers from a variety of materials

Creating the Background

Materials:

blue, brown, red, pink, green, and yellow construction paper

simple border (optional)

scissors

stapler

flowered wrapping paper

bulletin-board letters (worksheets on pages 64 and 65)

flower-part patterns and labels (worksheets on pages 66 and 67)

Procedure:

1. Back a bulletin board with blue construction paper. Add a simple border if desired.

2. Staple a sheet of brown construction paper along the bottom of the bulletin board to represent a table. Staple a vase or flowerpot cut from red construction paper on the brown paper.

3. Trace and cut out the flower-part patterns and labels. Staple the flower parts to the board to the right of the table. Save the labels for placement on the bulletin board after completing the third exploration activity.

4. Trace and cut out bulletin-board letters from flowered wrapping paper to spell the word *flowers*. Staple the letters vertically along the right side of the bulletin board.

5. Trace and cut out bulletin-board letters to make the title "A Bouquet for Parents." Staple the title near the top of the bulletin board.

Exploring the Topic

1. Ask younger students to name as many parts of a flower as they can think of. Write their answers on the chalkboard. Then show the class a real flower with the roots attached. Compare the list on the chalkboard with the parts of the actual flower. Explain that all flowers have the same basic parts—petals, stems, roots, and leaves. Each is important in helping the plant grow and produce new plants. Briefly explain the basic functions of each plant part. If possible, provide a variety of real flowers with attached roots for the class to examine.

2. For an on-going project, place a flowering plant in a dirt-filled clear plastic pot. Encourage students to watch the plant as it grows. Explain that this project will take time before children actually see any results. Invite students to be responsible for collecting data. On a classroom chart, include information, such as the number of leaves, the height of the plant, and the number of flowers. Over a two to four-week period, have different students responsible for recording growth information and watering the plant. Remind the youngsters to watch the roots grow, too.

3. If possible, provide a variety of real flowers for students to dissect and explore. Divide the class into small cooperative-learning groups. Give each group a flower and a sheet of newspaper. Instruct the students to carefully remove the petals from the flowers and then look closely for the flower parts modeled and displayed on the bulletin board. Have an adult circulate around the groups with a knife to slice open the pistils to reveal the ovaries inside.

4. As children examine the flowers, encourage students to discuss the flower parts they find. As each part is discussed, staple a label to the corresponding flower part on the bulletin board. Help the students discover that all flowers have the same essential parts. In classrooms with younger students, use only labels and flower parts that have been talked about in class.

5. Duplicate the worksheet provided on page 68. Invite students to work together in small cooperative-learning groups to complete the worksheet. This worksheet is designed for older students, but can be used in primary classrooms, too. On a master worksheet, omit the labels for the flower parts that have not yet been introduced.

6. Point out that all flowers have parts in common because these parts are necessary for the plant's survival. Encourage students to predict the function of each flower part. Then assign small groups of students to work together as investigative teams to research the functions of the various flower parts. Assign a different flower part to each team. Provide time for the teams to present their findings to their classmates. Encourage team members to discuss how the absence of the part they researched would affect the flowers.

Applying Ideas

1. Invite students to create their own imaginary flowers. They may use the flower-part patterns provided on page 66, the flower art ideas provided on page 69, or their own designs. Remind students to include all the flower parts labeled on the bulletin board.

2. Have students share their flower examples with the class. Suggest that students point out the separate parts of the flowers as well as any special flower features. Encourage students to give their flowers names. Use the following questions about parts of flowers to encourage further discussion. Then invite students to add their completed flowers to the vase or flowerpot on the bulletin board.

> Which parts of the flower are helpful in food production or absorption?
>
> Which parts of the flower are helpful for reproduction?
>
> How are flowers helpful to the environment?

Integrating Other Subject Areas

Art

1. Invite students to use a variety of mediums to create 3-dimensional examples of flowers.

2. If possible, arrange for the class to visit a floral shop (or invite a florist to come visit the classroom). Ask the florist to demonstrate flower arranging.

Health

1. Suggest that students make a paper flower garden for the walls of a local nursing home or for a person or family in need of a little cheer.

2. Help the students compare the parts of flowers and their functions with similar parts and functions of the human body.

3. Point out that some flowers are harmful to people and animals if specific flower parts are ingested or eaten. Challenge students to research flowers that have harmful parts. Suggest that students make a chart to share their findings with the class.

4. Encourage students to discuss the roles flowers play in the lives of people. Point out the psychological and therapeutic benefits of flowers.

Language Arts

1. Ask students the difference between the care of real flowers and that of their bulletin-board flowers. Invite students to write paragraphs about the names, planting seasons, and care of their imaginary flowers. Place the descriptions in a pocket on the bulletin board. Encourage students to read the descriptions independently.

2. Encourage students to write creative stories about a world where flowers do not exist.

Music

Ask the music teacher to introduce the students to songs about flowers, such as "The Yellow Rose of Texas," "The Rose," "Tiptoe Through the Tulips," and so on.

Social Studies

1. Have students research to find out the name of their state flower. Just for fun, sponsor a contest to select a class flower. Students might choose from the flower models they made for the bulletin board.

2. Encourage interested students to discover the many ways that flowers are used in different cultures around the world, such as for holiday celebrations or for decoration. Discuss how certain flowers are symbolic—tulips represent the Netherlands, lilies are associated with Easter, and so on.

Spelling

Encourage the students to become familiar with the parts of the flower by adding these words to their weekly spelling lists.

Pollution Solutions

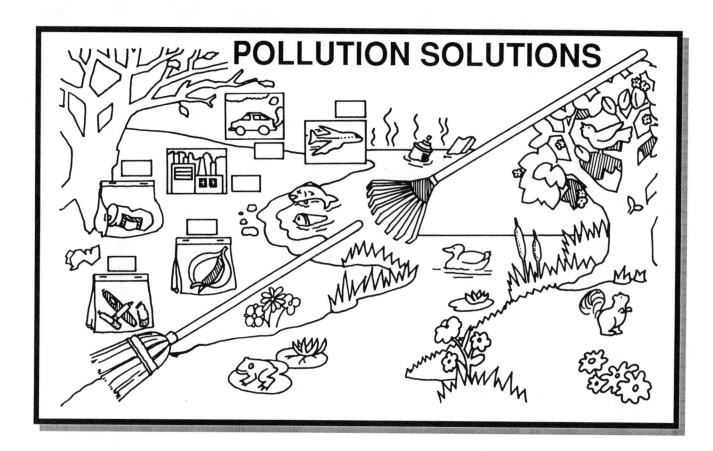

All living things need clean and safe environments in order to thrive, whether that environment be in the form of land, water, or air. When any of these forms are polluted, the environment as a whole suffers, and living things, including human life, are affected dramatically. Focusing students' attention on the problems associated with pollution may help them begin to think about possible solutions as responsible citizens on this Earth.

As students create this bulletin board together, they will:

- explore the types of pollution found in the school neighborhood

- sort pollutants according to danger levels and type

- generate possible solutions to pollution problems

Creating the Background

Materials:

yellow, blue, green, and brown construction paper

scissors

stapler

bulletin-board letters (worksheets on pages 64 and 65)

Procedure:

1. Back a bulletin board with yellow construction paper.

2. Draw and cut out a broom and rake from brown construction paper. Staple the items diagonally across the bulletin board.

3. Cut shapes from construction paper to represent blue water, brown and green hills, and green trees.

4. Trace and cut out bulletin-board letters to make the title "Pollution Solutions." Staple the title near the top of the bulletin board.

Exploring the Topic

1. For younger students, divide the class into two or three groups. Give each group a paper trash bag and each student a set of disposable, plastic gloves. Invite students to walk around the school grounds picking up trash. Have one member of each group carry a separate bag for items that may be recyclable. Be sure students wash their hands with soap and water after touching any trash. After returning to the classroom, encourage a discussion about the types of trash, areas where the most trash was found, and which items are recyclable.

2. Give each student a sheet of paper, a pencil, and a paper trash bag. Then take the students outside on a tour of the school grounds to collect forms of pollution. Before leaving the classroom, give each student a pair of plastic, disposable gloves to wear when picking up trash. Stress safety. Instruct students to collect only those items that are safe and to leave dangerous items for the school-maintenance crew to dispose of at another time. Ask students or a student helper to record each pollutant students collect and where the pollutant was found. Encourage students to record invisible forms of pollution as well, such as car exhaust or smoke from the school smokestack. Return to the classroom when each student has collected and written about several items. Remind students to wash their hands with soap and water.

3. Divide the class into small cooperative-learning groups to share the contents of their bags. Discuss the examples of pollution found by the students and the hazards of each type. Items might be rated according to danger level or sorted by type, such as paper, metal, and so on. Use questions like the following to encourage further discussion:

    Which type of pollution do you think is most hazardous? Why?

    How do you think these pollutants might be made less hazardous to the environment? (Examples might be making pollutants biodegradable, providing more trash receptacles, more trash collectors, and so on.)

    How can you help make the environment cleaner and safer?

4. Challenge students to sort the trash they collect into items that may be recycled (aluminum cans, newspaper), items that are biodegradable (banana peels, grass clippings), and items that are pollutants (motor oil, batteries). Provide plastic gloves for the students who handle the trash. Spread newspapers on the tables.

Applying Ideas

1. Invite students to place their trash items in small resealable plastic bags. Remind students to wash their hands immediately after touching the trash. For those items that are unsuitable to keep in the classroom or for those pollutants that are invisible, suggest that students draw or make pollution models. Have students staple the bags of trash, drawings, and models to the bulletin board. Encourage students to write the date and places where the pollutants were found on 3" x 5" index cards. Staple the cards next to the appropriate pollutants on the bulletin board.

2. Invite each student to select one pollutant of special concern to use as a basis for writing a creative story from the point of view of the trash. Suggest that students write about how the pollutant arrived on the school grounds, how it feels to be a pollutant, and so on. Have students create happy endings for their stories by suggesting prevention techniques or safe ways to recycle and dispose of trash. Compile the stories into a booklet entitled "Solutions to Pollution." Place the booklet near or on the bulletin board for students to read independently.

3. Sponsor a recycling center in the classroom. Designate separate trash containers for paper items, glass items, and metal items. Encourage students to place trash items found on the school grounds in the appropriate containers. Discuss the results at one-week intervals. Conduct an awareness campaign throughout the school of the results.

4. Recycling does not have to end with cleaning up the school grounds. Encourage students to place recyclable items from the classroom in recycling-center containers. Also, encourage the administration to set up a school-wide recycling program concentrating on recycling used paper.

Art

Invite the students to make posters encouraging others to keep the environment clean. Classrooms are environments, too. Make posters urging students to clean up their classrooms.

Math

1. Have students collect discarded paper from their classroom each week. At the end of the week, have students place the paper on a bathroom scale and weigh the approximate amount of paper thrown away that week. Record the weight on a classroom chart. An alternative activity is to weigh the amount of paper used each day. At the end of the week, add the five figures together to come up with a total amount of paper thrown away in a week's time.

Monday	Tuesday	Wednesday	Thursday	Friday	
10 lbs	+ 5 lbs	+ 10 lbs	+ 12 lbs	+ 3 lbs	= 40 lbs

2. Have students calculate the number of waste items generated in a school day, such as the number of milk cartons, worksheets, food wastes, and so on. Suggest that students consult the janitor and other school personnel for help in gathering data. Help students make a graph of the results to share with other teachers and students in the school.

3. Help the students graph the results of their pollution walk. Provide a variety of art materials for students to use to design and make posters that will prevent further pollution of the items graphed. Display the posters throughout the school. Then have small groups of students conduct other pollution walks two to three times per week to see if the posters have a positive impact on students. Graph and share those results with the student population.

Social Studies

1. Invite the class to write a letter to the Environmental Protection Agency. Encourage students to ask questions about the environment and what they can do to stop pollution. Send letters to the following:

   > U. S. Environmental Protection Agency
   > Office of Communications and Public Affairs
   > 401 M St. SW, PM211B
   > Washington, DC 20460

2. Encourage interested students to discuss ways that pollution affects society at large. Students may also write futuristic descriptions of problems created in the United States because of pollution, or ways the problems of pollution may be solved in the future.

3. If possible, arrange for the class to visit a waste disposal plant and observe the process necessary to dispose of waste materials produced by communities. Point out the types of recycling measures used. Encourage students to ask questions of the employees and discover ways to be less "waste producing."

Animal Race

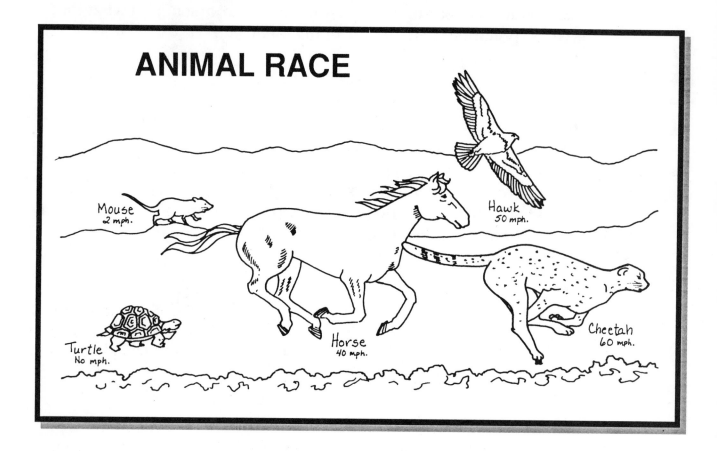

ANIMAL RACE

Mouse
2 mph.

Hawk
50 mph.

Turtle
No mph.

Horse
40 mph.

Cheetah
60 mph.

There are as many different kinds of animals as there are types of people. Each animal has special adaptations that make it better suited to live in a particular environment. For example, most skin coverings protect animals from the elements, the mouth and teeth allow animals to eat the type of food they need for survival, and muscular structure accommodates the roles of both hunter and prey. Most students find the study of animals fascinating. As students begin to note comparisons between different animals, they will discover more of the similarities between themselves and all living things.

As students create this bulletin board together, they will:

- discover how fast different animals can move or run

- explore how different animals adapt to different environments

- research animals of their choices

- compare animal and human traits

Creating the Background

Materials:

brown, tan, sky blue, and a deep-blue construction paper

stapler

blue tissue paper (optional)

bulletin-board letters (worksheets on pages 64 and 65)

Procedure:

1. Back a bulletin board with sky blue construction paper.

2. Tear sheets of tan construction paper and brown construction paper along the top edges. Staple the tan paper on the bottom half of the bulletin board. Position the brown paper on top of the tan paper along the bottom third of the bulletin board.

3. Cut scallops along the top edge of deep-blue construction paper. Staple the sheets on the bottom fourth of the bulletin board. (You may wish to substitute blue crumpled tissue paper.)

4. Trace and cut out bulletin-board letters to make the title "Animal Race." Staple the title near the top of the bulletin board.

Exploring the Topic

1. Invite students to brainstorm a list of animals. Write the list on the chalkboard. Point out that some animals are able to run faster than other animals, just as some people are able to run faster than other people. Have students choose the fastest and the slowest animals. Then provide reference materials for students to use to research the speeds of different animals. Help students graph the results, if appropriate.

2. Display pictures of a variety of animals around the classroom. Include animals from different habitats—birds, fish, reptiles, and mammals. Invite interested students to share what they know about the animal pictures. Use questions like the following to encourage further discussion. Ask students to provide reasons for their answers as well.

   Which animals travel on land? Air? Water?

   Which animals are probably meat eaters? Plant eaters?

   Which animals live in warm climates? Cold climates?
   Dry climates? Damp climates?

3. Explain that certain human behaviors are sometimes identified with particular animals. For example, a person might be described as "stubborn as a mule." Help the students brainstorm a list of other animals with comparative human traits. A partial list is provided here.

   bear — hungry   mouse — quiet

   bull — mean   owl — wise

   deer — timid   ox — strong

   dolphin — friendly   swan — graceful

   fox — sly   turtle — slow

   lion — brave

Applying Ideas

1. Invite the students to draw and cut out pictures of their animals to staple on the bulletin board according to their comparative speeds—from slowest to fastest. Have the students record the speed of each animal under the corresponding animal picture.

2. Invite each student to select an animal to research. Ask students to take notes about the animals' sizes, types of habitats, food preferences, enemies, and so on. Have students use the worksheet on page 70 to record interesting animal facts.

3. Invite students to share information about their animals with the rest of the class. Staple each animal recording sheet near the animal it describes. Encourage students to consider which animals they are most like and why. Graph the results. Display the graph near the bulletin board.

Integrating Other Subject Areas

Art

Invite students to create pictures of their animals in various environments using a variety of mediums, such as watercolor, tempera paints, markers, and so on. Encourage students to share as many facts about their animals as possible through their drawings. Display the pictures in the classroom. Help students uncover the "hidden facts" about the different animals.

Music

Sing favorite animal songs. After each song, brainstorm a list of information the song reveals about animals.

Physical Education

Help the Physical Education teacher organize an Animal Trivia Olympics. Each activity offered might state an animal fact as an incentive. For example, the long jump statement might read, "A frog can jump up to four feet." A track statement might read, "A duck could run this distance in two minutes," and so on. Encourage students to try to do their best in the different Olympic events. Reward each student for his or her participation.

Camouflage

Camouflage is one way animals adapt to their environment. The colorings and markings on an animal help "hide" it from hunters and other predators. Some animals change their coloring and markings to blend with the surroundings of each new season. Noting the camouflage of each animal helps students appreciate the many ways nature and animals are in harmony.

As students create this bulletin board together, they will:

- explore the importance of camouflage

- create camouflages for animals in a variety of habitats

Creating the Background

Materials:

various colors of construction paper—light blue, gray, tan, brown, shades of green

white tissue paper

bulletin-board letters (worksheets on pages 64 and 65)

Procedure:

1. Back a bulletin board with light blue construction paper.

2. Staple mountains cut from gray or tan construction paper on the bulletin board. Crumple tissue paper to make snowcaps and clouds.

3. Cut fringe along one edge of different shades of green construction paper to make grass. Staple the "grass" at different heights on the bulletin board. Position the darker shades behind the lighter shades.

4. Staple scalloped sheets of blue construction paper along the bottom of the bulletin board for water.

5. Complete the background by stapling sheets of light brown construction paper on the bulletin board to create a "dirt" foreground. Slightly incline the ground.

6. Staple a tree cut from construction paper on the right side of the bulletin board. Add fall leaves for contrast.

7. Trace and cut out bulletin-board letters to make the title "Camouflage." Staple the title near the top of the bulletin board.

Exploring the Topic

1. Give each student a lizard pattern to cut out and color with bright colors (worksheet on page 71). Take the students outside to hide their lizards. Then divide the class into small cooperative-learning groups. Challenge each group to take turns finding all the lizards within a designated time limit. Encourage the students to discuss what they might do to the lizards to make them harder to find. Give the students other lizard patterns to cut out and color in shades that blend with the environment. Invite the students to hide these lizards. Compare the times groups take to find the camouflaged lizards with the times required for them to find the brightly colored lizards. Ask questions like the following to encourage further discussion:

   Which lizards were easier to find, the brightly colored lizards or the camouflaged lizards? Why?

   Which lizards were most difficult to find? Why?

   How is camouflage helpful to animals?

2. Help students brainstorm a list of animals that are common to the area where they live. Invite students to research favorite animals to discover the animals' habitats, food supplies, predators, and protective colorings and markings. Provide time for students to share the information they discover in class. Discuss the variety of ways nature provides protection for the young of each species.

Applying Ideas

1. Direct students' attention to the bulletin board. Explain that camouflage is a form of protection for insects and animals. Show students several pictures of creatures that use camouflage to blend into their environment, such as chameleons, walking sticks, arctic hares, or zebras. Discuss which animals might live in the habitats portrayed on the bulletin board.

2. Have each student choose one animal to draw and color to blend in with its environment. Then cut out and staple the animal to the bulletin board. Remind students that their animals should appear to blend in with the bulletin-board environment. When the bulletin board is complete, challenge students to find all the camouflaged animals.

3. Provide a variety of art supplies for students to use to invent unique animals that might live in the habitats depicted on the bulletin board. Remind students to consider the types of camouflage and other adaptations necessary for the animals' protection.

4. Have students write brief descriptions of how the colorings and markings of their animals protect them. Compile the descriptions into a booklet to place near the bulletin board for students' reading enjoyment.

Integrating Other Subject Areas

Art

Invite students to design camouflage outfits for themselves in familiar settings, such as their bedrooms, the classroom, and so on.

Language Arts

1. Share *Just So Stories* by Rudyard Kipling (Holt, 1985) with the students. Encourage interested students to write tales describing how the leopard got its spots, the deer got its white tail, and other similar stories.

2. Invite students to write stories about the advantages of being able to camouflage oneself in familiar surroundings (see the art activity above).

Social Studies

Explain that hunters and members of the armed forces wear camouflage outfits at certain times to intentionally make it difficult to be seen. Encourage students to discuss when being camouflaged would be helpful.

Dinosaur Land

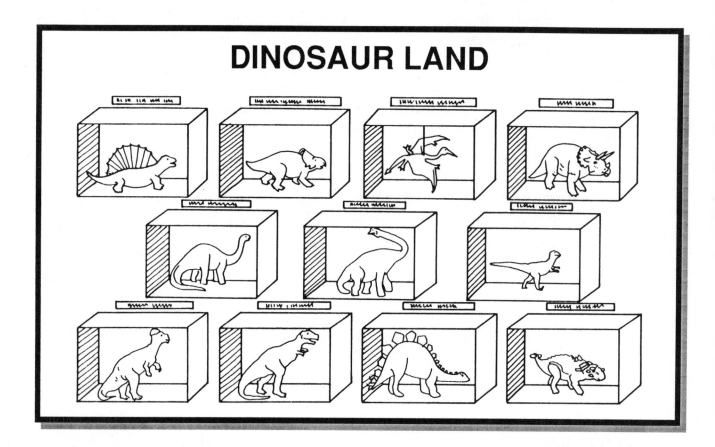

Dinosaurs are an interesting key to the past for all students. Scientists have learned much about the Earth and its inhabitants millions of years ago through the study of dinosaur artifacts. And although no one knows for certain what these unusual creatures actually looked like, students will find the possibilities intriguing. Asking students to predict why dinosaurs eventually became extinct may encourage them to begin to appreciate the importance of taking care of the Earth and all of its precious species.

As students create this bulletin board together, they will:

- explore the many ways dinosaurs may be classified

- write dinosaur reports

- create dioramas for specific dinosaurs

Creating the Background

Materials:

black construction paper

simple border (optional)

stapler

bulletin-board letters (worksheets on pages 64 and 65)

Procedure:

1. Back a bulletin board with black construction paper.

2. Staple a simple border around the outside edge if desired.

3. Trace and cut out bulletin-board letters to make the title "Dinosaur Land." Staple the title near the top of the bulletin board.

Exploring the Topic

1. Invite students to share what they know about dinosaurs. Show the students pictures of a variety of different dinosaurs. Write the names of the dinosaurs on strips of tagboard. Use the name strips to help students review the names of the dinosaurs.

2. Divide the class into small, cooperative-learning groups. Distribute the dinosaur name strips evenly among the groups. Explain that dinosaurs may be grouped according to their diets. Meat-eating dinosaurs have sharp teeth and claws. Plant-eating dinosaurs have flat teeth for grinding plants. Show the students a picture of each type of dinosaur. Challenge the groups to use informational books as needed to sort the name strips they received into meat-eating and plant-eating groups. Suggest that students draw pictures of each dinosaur they research as well. Compile the information from all the groups on a large chart.

Applying Ideas

1. Invite students to select favorite dinosaurs to research further. Suggest that students find information about the sizes of dinosaurs, when and where the dinosaurs lived, and other interesting facts. Compile the research papers into a booklet about dinosaurs. Place the booklet near the bulletin board for students to read independently.

2. Ask students to bring shoeboxes to school to use for making dioramas. Provide a variety of colors of construction paper and other art supplies for students to use to make background details that show the specific habitats of the dinosaurs.

3. Have students draw and cut out pictures of the dinosaurs they research to place in their shoebox dioramas.

4. Help students pin or staple their dioramas on the prepared bulletin board. Have each student make a label for his or her dinosaur as well. Invite students to share their research reports and dioramas together in class. Use questions like the following to encourage further discussion:

    Which dinosaurs were meat-eaters? Plant-eaters?

    Which dinosaurs were the largest in size? Smallest?

    What do you think happened that caused dinosaurs to become extinct?

Integrating Other Subject Areas

Art

1. Create a dinosaur mural on butcher paper. Have each student choose a dinosaur to draw. Remind students to draw their dinosaurs in different environments.

2. Invite interested students to create 3-dimensional papier-mâché models of each type of dinosaur.

Language Arts

1. Invite students to write stories about what might happen if a dinosaur were to visit their classroom.

2. Ask the school librarian to suggest books and stories about dinosaurs for the students to enjoy reading. Make a dinosaur book display in the classroom. Then sponsor a Dinosaur Read-a-thon. Some suggestions may include *Dinosaurs and More Dinosaurs* (M. Jean Craig, Scholastic, 1973), *Dinosaurs* (Mary Clark, Childrens Press, 1981) or *Dinosaur Time* (Peggy Parish, Harper & Row, 1983). Give students a dinosaur cutout for each dinosaur book they read. Provide time for students to share their favorite stories and dinosaur facts in class.

Math

1. Take the students outside to a large open area. Help the students measure and mark off the lengths of the different dinosaurs. Encourage students to brainstorm familiar objects in their world that are the same size as some of the dinosaurs.

2. Help students make a graph or chart to compare the dimensions of different dinosaurs.

Spelling

1. Encourage younger children to choose adjectives that describe dinosaurs to add to their spelling lists, such as scary, scaly, or claws.

2. Encourage students to use the names of dinosaurs in their spelling lists for an extra challenge!

Oceans

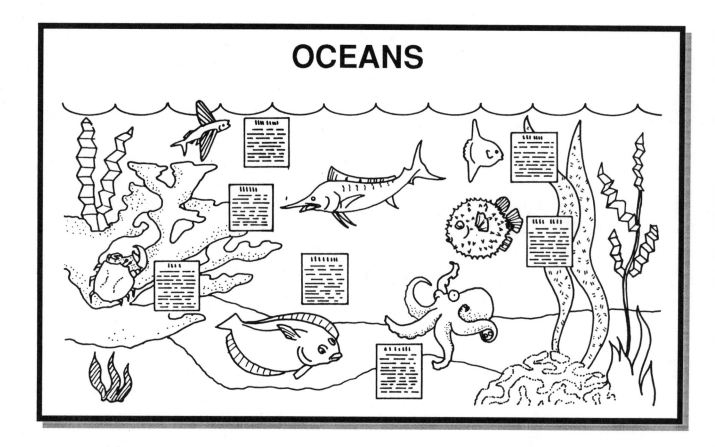

There are five oceans on the planet Earth—Pacific, Atlantic, Arctic, Antarctic, and Indian. A variety of fascinating sea creatures and plants inhabit these waters. Each species has specific physical characteristics that enable it to co-exist with other sea creatures. Sea creatures must adapt to the places they occupy in the ocean as well. Some creatures live in the dark lower depths, others reside in the middle strata of water, while still others prefer the warmer surface waters. Students may begin to see the similarities between the adaptations of all creatures, whether they live on land, in the air, or in the water.

As students create this bulletin board together, they will:

- explore the variety of sea creatures found in oceans

- categorize sea creatures into plankton, nekton, and benthos

- draw pictures of different groups of sea creatures

Creating the Background

Materials:

blue butcher paper

simple border (optional)

light-blue tissue paper

brown and green construction paper

stapler

bulletin-board letters (worksheets on pages 64 and 65)

Procedure:

1. Back a bulletin board with blue butcher paper.

2. Staple a simple border around the outside edge if desired.

3. Staple crinkled light-blue tissue paper over the bulletin board (leave a few inches at the top). Shape the top edge of the tissue paper to look like waves.

4. Cut seaweed from green construction paper to staple on the sides of the bulletin board. Bend some of the strips to create a 3-dimensional effect. Cover the bottom of the bulletin board with brown paper to look like a sandy ocean floor.

5. Trace and cut out bulletin-board letters to make the title "Oceans." Staple the title near the top of the bulletin board.

Exploring the Topic

1. Show the younger students a variety of pictures of sea creatures. Then invite them to share what they know about oceans and the sea creatures that live there. Create three categories on the chalkboard—plants and creatures that float around (jellyfish), fish that swim around freely (dolphins, octopus), and creatures and plants that live on the ocean bottom (oysters, coral). Have the students try to sort the pictures into the various categories.

2. Invite students to share what they know about oceans and the sea creatures that live there. Record the sea creatures the students name on strips of tagboard. Then write the words *plankton, nekton,* and *benthos* along the top of the chalkboard. Explain that sea creatures may be grouped into these three categories. Challenge students to use encyclopedias and dictionaries to discover the meanings of these three terms.

   Plankton: Plants and sea creatures that float and drift about, such as jellyfish and arrowworms.

   Nekton: Free-swimming creatures, such as species of fish, sharks, and dolphins.

   Benthos: Sea creatures and plants that live on the bottom of the ocean, such as oysters and coral.

3. Invite students to predict under which category on the chalkboard each sea creature name strip should be placed. Then have students work independently or in small cooperative-learning groups to research and check the accuracy of their predictions.

4. Show the students a globe or map of the world. Help them locate the Pacific, Atlantic, Arctic, Antarctic, and Indian Oceans. Encourage students to research answers to questions like the following about the oceans. Challenge students to research and share other ocean trivia as well.

   What percentage of the world is covered by water? (70%)

   What percentage of surface water is salt water? (97%)

   Which sea creatures are mammals?

Which oceans border the continental United States?

Which is the largest ocean?

Applying Ideas

1. Show younger students a variety of sea creatures. Have each student draw his or her favorite. Cut out and then staple the pictures on the bulletin board. Remind students to place their creatures in the appropriate environment in the ocean—oysters or coral should be placed on the bottom of the bulletin board, for example. Help the children label their sea creatures. Challenge students to write brief reports about their underwater friends, if appropriate.

2. Show students pictures of a variety of sea creatures. Then invite each student to select a favorite sea creature to research. Encourage students to find out where in the ocean their creatures reside and the physical characteristics that help their creatures adapt to their ocean environments.

3. Have each student draw and cut out a picture of the sea creature he or she researches. Provide time for students to share their drawings and reports in class.

4. Help students staple the pictures of their sea creatures and the accompanying reports on the appropriate parts of the bulletin-board ocean.

Integrating Other Subject Areas

Art

1. Invite students to create their own new variety of sea creature. Add the new pictures to the bulletin-board ocean. Challenge classmates to guess which sea creatures are real and which are imaginary.

2. Invite interested students to create 3-dimensional papier-mâché models of different types of sea creatures.

3. Obtain Styrofoam meat trays from the supermarket. Help the students cut the trays into fish shapes. Then encourage students to use pencils and other objects to make interesting scale impressions on the Styrofoam fish. Show the students how to roll an even coat of paint over the scale impressions. Place the fish painted-side down on sheets of construction paper. Carefully press down on the fish shapes. Then carefully remove the shapes to reveal fish prints.

Math

1. Create story problems for your students to solve using sea creatures as examples or for practice with simple equations.

2. Help students make a graph or chart to compare the sizes of the five oceans.

3. Challenge students to write story problems involving facts about the ocean and sea creatures.

Language Arts

Invite students to choose a real or imaginary sea creature. Write a simple story about what it would be like to be that creature. An alternative activity would include having students write descriptions of their sea creatures. Combine all the stories or descriptions into a class booklet titled "A School of Fish." Place the booklet in the reading center.

Spelling

1. Encourage students to use the names of sea creatures in their spelling lists for an extra challenge!

2. Have students alphabetize a list of sea creatures.

Smorgasbord of Classy Foods

SMORGASBORD OF CLASSY FOODS

Breakfast

Lunch

Dinner

In this day of fast-food restaurants and convenience foods, it is especially important for students to learn about good nutrition and eating habits. Eating well-balanced meals leads to good health. A variety of foods are needed to supply the body with the different substances it needs to do its work and to grow. Students who learn about good nutrition at an early age are more likely to practice good eating habits all their lives.

As students create this bulletin board together, they will:

● explore a variety of foods

● plan balanced meals

● make models of balanced meals

Creating the Background

Materials:

>   yellow and brown construction paper
>
>   simple border (optional)
>
>   stapler
>
>   bulletin-board letters (worksheets on pages 64 and 65)

Procedure:

1. Back a bulletin board with yellow construction paper.

2. Staple a simple border around the outside edge if desired.

3. Staple sheets of brown construction paper vertically on the bulletin board to make three long tables. Write "Breakfast" below the first table and "Lunch" and "Dinner" below the second and third tables, respectively.

4. Trace and cut out bulletin-board letters to make the title "Smorgasbord of Classy Foods." Staple the title near the top of the bulletin board.

Exploring the Topic

1. Help students brainstorm a list of their favorite foods. Write the foods the students name on strips of tagboard. Discuss the USDA's Food Guide Pyramid with the students—fruits; vegetables; breads and cereals; dairy products; and meat, fish, poultry, and eggs. Write the food group names across the top of the chalkboard. Help the students categorize and place the food name strips under the correct headings.

2. Survey the class to determine the students' favorite foods for each food group. Discuss why some foods are preferred over others.

3. Send a note home to parents asking them to help their children keep track of the foods they eat for one week. At the end of the week, invite students to select their favorite meals. Help the students evaluate the meals to see if they are well-balanced and contain foods representative of all five food groups. Ask the students questions like the following to encourage further discussion:

Which food group(s) do most of the foods you enjoy eating come from? Why do you suppose this is so?

Are all the meals you eat well-balanced? Why or why not?

Are there food group(s) from which you need to eat more foods to maintain a balanced diet? Which ones?

Applying Ideas

1. In classrooms with younger students, plan several well-balanced meals as a class activity. Have students suggest food items from each of the five food groups to be included in a breakfast, a lunch, and a dinner.

2. Divide the class into three groups. Have the members of one group plan well-balanced breakfast menus, the members of another group plan well-balanced lunch menus, and members of the last group plan well-balanced dinner menus. Ask students to draw, cut out pictures of foods, or use dried foods to represent the different foods in the meals they plan. Then have the students glue the items on paper plates. Staple the paper plate "meals" on the appropriate "tables" on the prepared bulletin board.

3. Suggest that students draw and cut out silverware, centerpieces, napkins, and other accessories to staple on the bulletin board to create a more festive presentation.

4. Explain that a daily balanced diet consists of the following number of servings from each of the five food groups. Have students plan balanced meals for a day. Encourage children to select foods they enjoy. Remind students to consider how the different foods complement each other at the meals as well. Discuss the finished menus together in class.

> 2–4 servings of fruits
>
> 3–5 servings of vegetables
>
> 6–11 servings of breads, cereals, rice, and pasta
>
> 2–3 servings of dairy products
>
> 2–3 servings of meat, fish, poultry, eggs, and nuts

Integrating Other Subject Areas

Art

1. Invite interested students to make food collages from pictures of foods they either draw or cut out from old magazines.

2. Discuss the role color plays in the presentation of foods. Encourage students to evaluate the meals they plan for color.

Language Arts

1. Invite students to write adjective-rich stories about favorite meals. Birthday, holiday, family celebrations, and other special occasion meals make interesting topics. Remind students to write about as many of their senses as possible—the smells, tastes, sights, sounds, and textures.

2. Have students select favorite foods to write food clues about. Use the descriptive clues to play a guessing game. Divide the class into two teams. Give each team 50 points to begin the game. Have team members take turns reading their food clues (one clue at a time) until the opposing team correctly identifies the food. Deduct points for each clue used. The team with the most points at the end of play is the winner.

Math

1. Challenge students with story problems to solve. Give each student a number of uncooked colored rotini noodles to use as counters to illustrate the problems.

2. Have students calculate the number of calories represented by each meal on the bulletin board. Help the students make comparisons between the caloric values of different meals.

Our Solar System

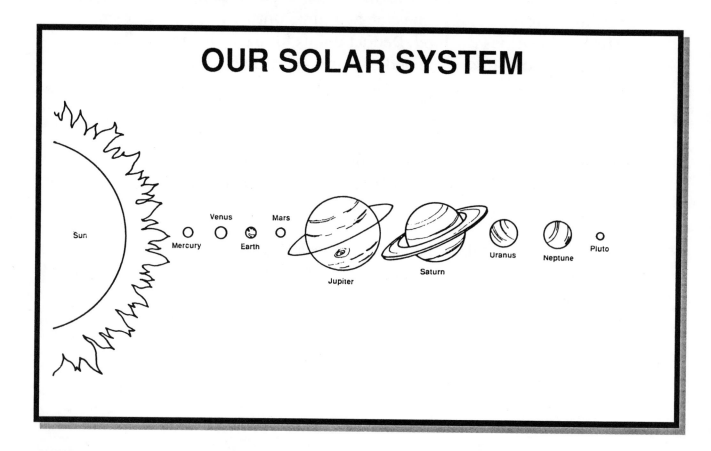

The solar system is a fascinating area of study for most students. Our solar system is made up of nine planets. The planets orbit around the sun at the same time they revolve around their own axes. Seven of the nine planets have moons that orbit around the planets. Other smaller masses, such as planetoids, stars, and smaller planets, are found in our solar system as well. Advanced space technology has enabled scientists to begin to explore and develop this vast frontier. A study of space will help students begin to realize the magnitude and immense opportunities for the expansion of the world in which they live.

As students create this bulletin board together, they will:

- explore the characteristics of the planets

- research various planets

- make a model of our solar system

Creating the Background

Materials:

black construction paper

yellow and orange tissue paper

stapler

bulletin-board letters (worksheets on pages 64 and 65)

Procedure:

1. Back a bulletin board with black construction paper.

2. Staple a large semi-circle cut from yellow tissue paper on the left side of the bulletin board. Make flames to staple around the sun's edge using crinkled yellow and orange tissue paper.

3. Trace and cut out bulletin-board letters to make the title "Our Solar System." Staple the title near the top of the bulletin board.

Exploring the Topic

1. Invite students to share what they know about our solar system and its planets. Show the students pictures of our solar system. Explain that our solar system is comprised of nine planets that revolve around the sun. Discuss the order of the planets and their distances from the sun.

2. Invite students to role-play the solar system. Make labels of the planets for participating students to wear. Obtain a large roll of adding-machine tape. Decide on a scale. Take the students outside to a large open area. Assign one student to role-play the sun. Ask that student to hold the end of the adding-machine tape. Unroll the tape and measure the distance of the planet Pluto from the sun using the predetermined scale. Have the student role-playing Pluto hold the tape at that marked location. Measure and mark the locations of the eight remaining planets along the tape. Have students stand next to their planets. When in position, suggest that students drop the tape and spin slightly (and carefully) as they move in oval-shaped orbits around the sun— without running into other "planets!"

Applying Ideas

1. Identify for younger students the nine planets—Mercury, Venus, Earth, Mars, Jupiter, Saturn, Uranus, Neptune, and Pluto. Divide the class into nine groups and assign a planet to each one. Have each group draw and cut out a paper model of their planet. Invite one group member to copy the name of the planet on a strip of tagboard. Staple the planet and the label in the correct order on the bulletin board.

1. Sun	6. Jupiter
2. Mercury	7. Saturn
3. Venus	8. Uranus
4. Earth	9. Neptune
5. Mars	10. Pluto

2. Divide the class into nine groups. Have each group research a different planet. Provide recording sheets for students to complete about the planets (worksheet on page 72).

3. Suggest that the members in each group use construction paper and other art supplies to make a scale model of their planet. Staple the models on the bulletin board in order based on distance from the sun.

4. Invite the members of each group to present information about their planets to the rest of the class. Ask students questions like the following to encourage further discussion:

> What do you think it would be like to live on Pluto? Compare the length of days, the climate, the size, and other comparisons that may be made to the planet Earth.

> Which planet is closest to the sun? Which is the farthest?

> Which planet is the smallest? Which is the largest?

> Which planet is the warmest? Which one is the coldest?

Integrating Other Subject Areas

Art

Invite interested students to create 3-dimensional papier-mâché models of the planets and their moons (if the planets have moons).

Language Arts

1. Encourage students to write stories about a visit to one of the planets. Suggest that they describe the scenery and climate.

2. Challenge students to make up acronyms to help them remember the order of the planets—My (Mercury) Very (Venus) Educated (Earth) Mother (Mars) Just (Juniper) Served (Saturn) Us (Uranus) Nine (Neptune) Pizzas (Pluto).

Math

Help students make a graph or chart to compare the sizes of the planets and their distances from the sun.

The Stars

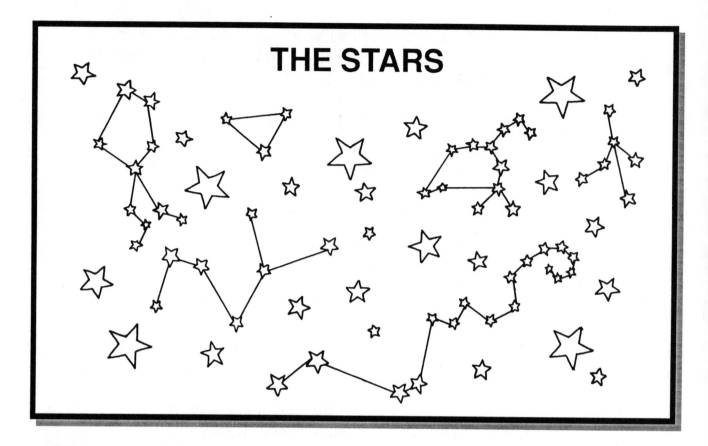

Although stars look like tiny points of light when viewed from Earth, they are actually huge balls of hot gases. All stars are so far away that the distances are measured in light years. Light travels six trillion miles in one year. People have studied the stars since the beginning of time. In ancient times, people used stars for navigation purposes. Locating different constellations helped travelers determine direction. The stars seemed to form certain patterns or pictures. The names these early astronomers gave to the various constellations are still in use today.

As students create this bulletin board together, they will:

- explore the different constellations

- create models of constellations

- research the legends associated with some of the constellations

- discover new constellations

Creating the Background

Materials:

black construction paper

simple border (optional)

stapler

bulletin-board letters (worksheets on pages 64 and 65)

Procedure:

1. Back a bulletin board with black construction paper.

2. Staple a simple border around the outside edge if desired.

3. Trace and cut out bulletin-board letters to make the title "The Stars." Staple the title near the top of the bulletin board.

Exploring the Topic

1. Invite students to share what they know about stars. Explain that stars are huge balls of gases. They look small because they are so far away from Earth. Invite students to predict how far away stars are. If possible, arrange to take the class to a planetarium.

2. Explain that ancient astronomers used the stars to navigate by. They did this by studying the locations of stars during different times of the year. They also noticed that many of the stars created pictures of familiar objects with their patterns. Show students pictures of some familiar constellations, such as the Big Dipper and the Little Dipper. Send a note home to parents explaining the activity. Ask parents to help their children locate the different constellations in the night sky. Then invite the students to study the skies on starry nights for a week or two to see if they can locate some of the constellations.

3. Divide the class into small cooperative-learning groups. Provide encyclopedias and other informational books about stars and constellations for groups to use to research the legends concerning the different constellations.

4. Give each group black construction paper, self-adhesive stars, and white chalk to use to make pictures of the constellations they research. Invite the members of each group to share the drawings of their constellations and the legends associated with each one with the rest of the class.

5. Ask students questions like the following to encourage further discussion:

   Which constellation is most interesting to you? Why?

   Why do you think early people were fascinated by the stars?

   Which constellations have you been able to locate in the night sky?

Applying Ideas

1. Invite each student to make four to six stars to staple on the prepared bulletin-board background. Students may use a star pattern (worksheet on page 73) or make a pattern of their own. Encourage students to make some stars different sizes to depict different distances from the Earth. Have students randomly staple their stars on the bulletin board.

2. Encourage small groups of students to take turns finding new constellations from the stars on the bulletin board. Have students use lengths of colored yarn to connect the stars that form the various constellations (use a different color for each constellation, if possible). Have groups complete an information form (worksheet on page 74) for each constellation they "discover." Include a variety of information, such as how many stars make up the new constellation, what does the constellation look like, and so on.

3. Provide time for students to discuss their constellations with the rest of the class. Compile the information forms into a booklet to place near the bulletin board. Challenge students to read about the different constellations and then try to locate each constellation on the board.

Integrating Other Subject Areas

Art

Invite interested students to use chalk to draw constellations on sheets of black construction paper. They may then use pins to carefully poke holes in their papers along the outlines of the constellations. Tape the paper constellations on a window or against a light source.

Language Arts

1. Invite each student to write several sentences describing his or her new constellation.

2. Encourage students to create legends about their original constellations to share with the rest of the class. Suggest that interested students present dramatic interpretations of their legends as well.

Math

1. Show the class a picture of the Big Dipper. Challenge the students to estimate the number of visible stars in this constellation. Invite students to look closely at the picture of the Big Dipper and count the actual stars. Compare the estimates with the actual number.

2. Explain that the distances of stars from Earth are measured in light years. Challenge students to use reference materials to help them define a light year. Then encourage students to research the distances of various stars from Earth. Help the students write these distances numerically!

Under a Microscope

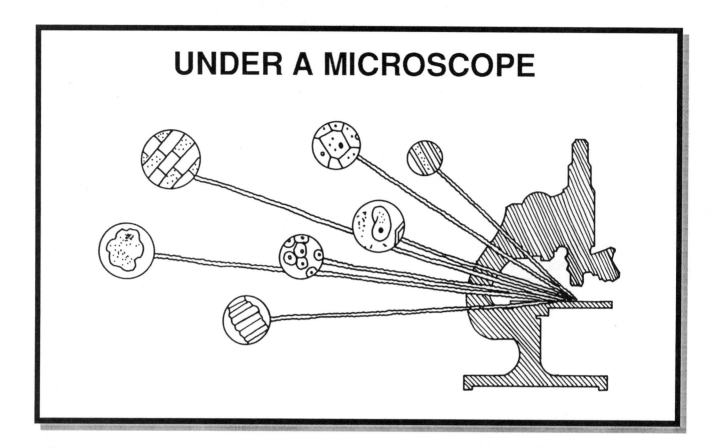

Many microscopic animals and particles are present in one drop of lake, river, or other bodies of water. A microscope magnifies these tiny animals and particles many times so that they may be seen by the human eye. Scientists are able to learn about bacteria and forms of viruses with the aid of microscopes. Microscopes will open up a whole new world to students. Note: This unit may be a little advanced for younger students.

As students create this bulletin board together, they will:

● explore various substances with a microscope

● make drawings of microscopic animals and particles as viewed under a microscope

Creating the Background

Materials:

    blue butcher paper

    black construction paper

    yarn

    stapler

    microscope pattern (worksheet on page 75)

    bulletin-board letters (worksheets on pages 64 and 65)

Procedure:

1. Back a bulletin board with blue butcher paper.

2. Trace and cut out a microscope from black construction paper to staple on the lower right-hand corner of the bulletin board.

3. Staple different lengths of yarn from the microscope to various places on the bulletin board (one length per student).

4. Trace and cut out bulletin-board letters to make the title "Under a Microscope." Staple the title near the top of the bulletin board.

Exploring the Topic

1. Have younger students experiment with looking at different objects beneath magnifying glasses. If you wish to increase the magnification, try taping two magnifying glasses together.

2. Show the students a clear glass of water. Encourage them to describe the water as completely as possible. When all ideas are exhausted, put a drop of the water on a microscope slide. Invite the students to take turns viewing the slide under a microscope. Encourage students to share their observations with the rest of the class.

3. Divide the class into small cooperative-learning groups. If possible, give each group a microscope and a variety of prepared slides. Invite students to take turns looking at the different slides under the microscopes. Encourage students to prepare slides of other substances to view under the microscopes as well. Discuss the different living and non-living particles. Ask students questions like the following to encourage further discussion:

> Describe some of the living creatures found on the slides.

> Describe other particles visible under the microscope.

> Which slide interests you the most? Why?

Applying Ideas

1. Invite students to select favorite slides to illustrate. Provide forms (worksheet on page 76) for the students to use to make their drawings. Have each student make two drawings of the slide he or she views. Remind students to label their drawings on the observation form. Encourage children to add color where appropriate.

2. Ask students to cut their observation sheets from the above activity in half. Have them cut out and then staple the top drawings on the prepared bulletin board. Collect the bottom halves of the forms to compile into a booklet entitled "Our Observations." Make a cover for the booklet (worksheet on page 77). Challenge students to study the drawings in the booklet and then find their matches on the bulletin board.

Integrating Other Subject Areas

Art

Invite students to draw colorful enlargements of slides viewed under the microscope. Help the students frame the drawings for display in the classroom.

Language Arts

1. Encourage students to write stories about what it might be like to live as an imaginary microscopic person.

2. Show students how to make box cameras (ask the school librarian for reference books). Then invite students to use the cameras to take close-up pictures of one small part of familiar objects. Ask the high-school photography class to develop the film. Display the photos in the classroom. Challenge students to try to identify the subject of each photo.

3. Encourage students to write haiku poems to place next to the photos they take in the activity described above.

What's the Matter?

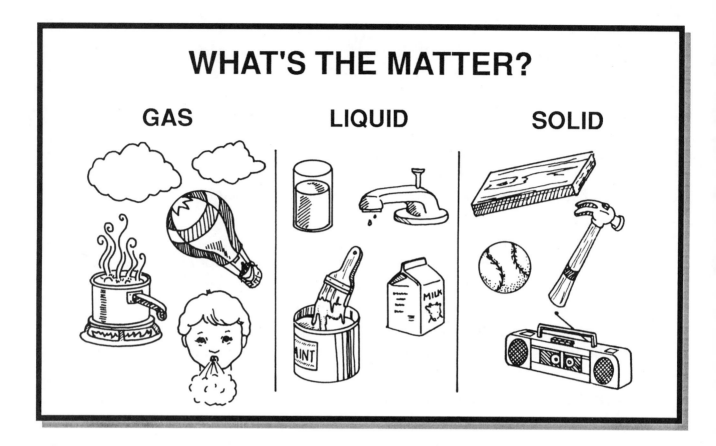

Matter is the name given to all things that take up space and have mass. There are three states of matter—liquids, solids, and gases. All matter exists in one of these three forms. Some matter can change from one form to another. Water, for example, can change from a liquid to a gas (steam) or to a solid (ice). The study of matter will help students see the importance and impact of changing states of matter on society and the world.

As students create this bulletin board together, they will:

- explore the different states of matter
- classify matter

Creating the Background

Materials:

blue butcher paper

simple border (optional)

stapler

bulletin-board letters (worksheets on pages 64 and 65)

Procedure:

1. Back a bulletin board with blue butcher paper.

2. Staple a simple border around the outside edge if desired.

3. Draw and cut out bulletin-board letters to make the words *liquid, solid,* and *gas*. Staple the words across the top of the bulletin board.

4. Trace and cut out bulletin-board letters to make the title "What's the Matter?" Staple the title near the top of the bulletin board.

Exploring the Topic

1. For younger children, explain that matter is everything that takes up space and has weight. Matter comes in three forms—solids, liquids, and gases. Solids refers to any item that does not change shape, such as a rock. Liquids do not have their own shape—they take the shape of the container they are in, such as juice in a bottle. Gases generally cannot be seen and they do not have a shape of their own, but they can fill large or small areas, such as a balloon. Encourage students to find examples of each form of matter in the classroom.

2. Help the students brainstorm a list of items found in the classroom. Challenge students to name items that cannot be seen, such as air, as well as items that are visible. Write the items the students name on strips of tagboard. Then divide the class into small cooperative-learning groups. Distribute the tagboard strips evenly among the different groups. Ask the members of each group to suggest several different ways to sort the items on the tagboard strips according to common properties.

3. Explain that all of the items written on the tagboard strips are called matter because they have mass and take up space. All matter is either a liquid, solid, or gas. Help the students group the tagboard strips into these three categories. Encourage groups to share their decisions with the rest of the class.

Applying Ideas

1. Divide the class into three groups. Have the members of one group draw, cut out pictures from old magazines, or make 3-dimensional models of several different solids. Assign the other two groups to do the same for liquids and gases, respectively. Be aware that the group working with gases may need help in finding pictures. Remind children that they can include pictures of objects that are inflated with air, such as balloons, beach balls, tires, and inflatable beach toys.

2. Gather all of the drawings, pictures, and models created in the above activity together on a table placed next to the bulletin board. Hold up one item at a time for students to discuss and then place under the appropriate category on the bulletin board.

3. Challenge students to identify those items on the bulletin board that may be changed from one form of matter to another. Discuss questions like the following to encourage further discussion:

> How do changes in temperature affect the states of matter of the items on the bulletin board?

Which solids on the bulletin board would change if a liquid were added to them?

Which state of matter changes form most quickly? More slowly? Can you give some examples?

Integrating Other Subject Areas

Language Arts

1. Encourage students to write stories about what it might feel like to be a solid or a gas changing into a liquid.

2. Discuss when it might be advantageous to be able to change form. Invite students to write about the advantages and disadvantages of changing form at will.

Math

1. Discuss the concepts of more and less. Challenge the students to predict whether one item is going to weigh more or less than another. For example, will a balloon filled with air weigh more or less than one filled with water, would an inflated balloon weigh more or less than an uninflated balloon, and so on. Encourage the students to come up with their own "more or less" questions.

2. Discuss the two properties of matter—mass and volume. Invite interested students to weigh different types of matter and calculate their volumes. Suggest that students compare the mass and volume of a liquid as it changes from a liquid to a solid. For example, have students weigh a cup of water and then freeze the water and weigh it again.

Physical Education

Invite students to move in ways that depict the three states of matter. Play music for each state—flowing music for liquids or marching music for solids, and so on.

Bullfrogs and Butterflies

All living things go through growth cycles. Some creatures, such as butterflies and frogs, go through dramatic physical changes. Butterflies go through four stages—from eggs, to caterpillars, to cocoons, before finally emerging as butterflies. Frogs begin their lives in water as tadpoles. As they grow into frogs, they are able to spend part of the time on land. Focusing students' attention on the dramatic growth cycles of these two creatures will help students begin to appreciate the dramatic changes that occur in their own growth cycles as well.

As students create this bulletin board together, they will:

- explore the meaning of metamorphosis

- create animals to represent various metamorphic stages

Creating the Background

Materials:

blue and green construction paper

blue and brown tissue paper

brown paper bag

stapler

markers or crayons

drawing paper

bulletin-board letters (worksheets on pages 64 and 65)

Procedure:

1. Back a bulletin board with blue construction paper.

2. Cut out a land shape and a pond shape from brown and blue tissue paper.

3. Cut out a tree trunk from a crumpled grocery bag to staple on the bulletin board. Staple free-form shapes cut from green construction paper on the trunk as a tree top.

4. Trace and cut out bulletin-board letters to make the title "Bullfrogs and Butterflies." Staple the title near the top of the bulletin board.

Exploring the Topic

1. Share the book *The Very Hungry Caterpillar* by Eric Carle (Putnam Publishing Group, 1969) with the class. Discuss the changes the caterpillar experiences in this story.

2. Show the class pictures of a variety of baby and adult animals. Encourage students to notice the changes that occur as animals grow older. Point out the similarities between baby and adult animals, too.

3. Explain that animals, like butterflies and bullfrogs, undergo a metamorphosis. Have students use dictionaries to find the meaning of this word. Challenge students to brainstorm a list of other animals (including humans) that undergo dramatic metamorphoses, too.

4. Help the students make a class "Metamorpho-list" on the chalkboard. Write the categories "Young" and "Mature" on the chalkboard. Then invite students to write the different stages of growth for various animals under the appropriate columns. For example, a student might write tadpole under the "Young" column and frog under the "Mature" column. Discuss how each animal, even a human being, undergoes changes during its life cycle.

5. Use the following questions to encourage further discussion:

    What purpose do growth cycles serve?

    During which stage are most animals vulnerable to their environment and predators?

    Which stage do you think is most interesting in the life cycle of butterflies? Bullfrogs? Why?

Applying Ideas

1. Ask younger students if they have ever seen a caterpillar, a cocoon, or a butterfly. Encourage students who have had any experience with butterflies to share with the class. Discuss with the students the four stages of a butterfly's life—egg, caterpillar, cocoon (pupa), and adult butterfly. Show pictures of each stage.

2. Help the students review the life cycle of a butterfly. Write each stage on the chalkboard. Invite volunteers to illustrate and label the different stages of growth—egg, caterpillar, cocoon, and butterfly.

3. Explain that frogs undergo rather dramatic changes in their life cycles as well. Trace the growth cycle of a frog. Help students compare the changes in the growth stages of butterflies with the growth stages of bullfrogs.

4. Divide the class into two groups. Assign one group to draw and cut out pictures depicting the stages of growth of a butterfly. Have the other group do the same for a bullfrog. Duplicate the patterns on pages 78–80, if desired. When the drawings are complete, invite the students to staple their drawings on the appropriate areas of the bulletin board.

5. Discuss how butterflies and bullfrogs are protected from their environment and predators during each stage of their life cycles (special colorations, type of habitat, time of season, and so on).

6. Challenge group members to work together to create protective habitats on the bulletin board for each stage of their creatures' life cycles. For example, place tissue paper over the frog eggs to represent mud and to make the eggs less visible, add leaves to the tree to hide the cocoon, cut tall grass from green and brown construction paper to protect the adult bullfrog, and so on.

Integrating Other Subject Areas

Language Arts

Ask students to write stories about the life cycles of animals from each animal's point of view. Encourage students to illustrate their stories as well. Compile the finished stories into a book entitled "Stages of Life." Place the book near the bulletin board for the students' reading enjoyment.

Social Studies

1. Invite students to bring in baby pictures and several recent photographs, too. Have each student look closely at his or her photos. Then ask students if they can see any differences in their pictures.

2. Invite students to discuss the different stages of human life represented in communities, such as infants, children, teenagers, young adults, adults, and senior citizens. Discuss the benefits each group brings to society. Point out the responsibilities society has to individuals at each stage of growth as well.

3. Encourage students to explore the types of services available within their community for different age groups. If possible, invite guest speakers from various service groups in the community to come visit the classroom and share how their agencies serve the needs of the different age groups.

Worksheets

A B C D

E F G H

I J K L M

N O P Q

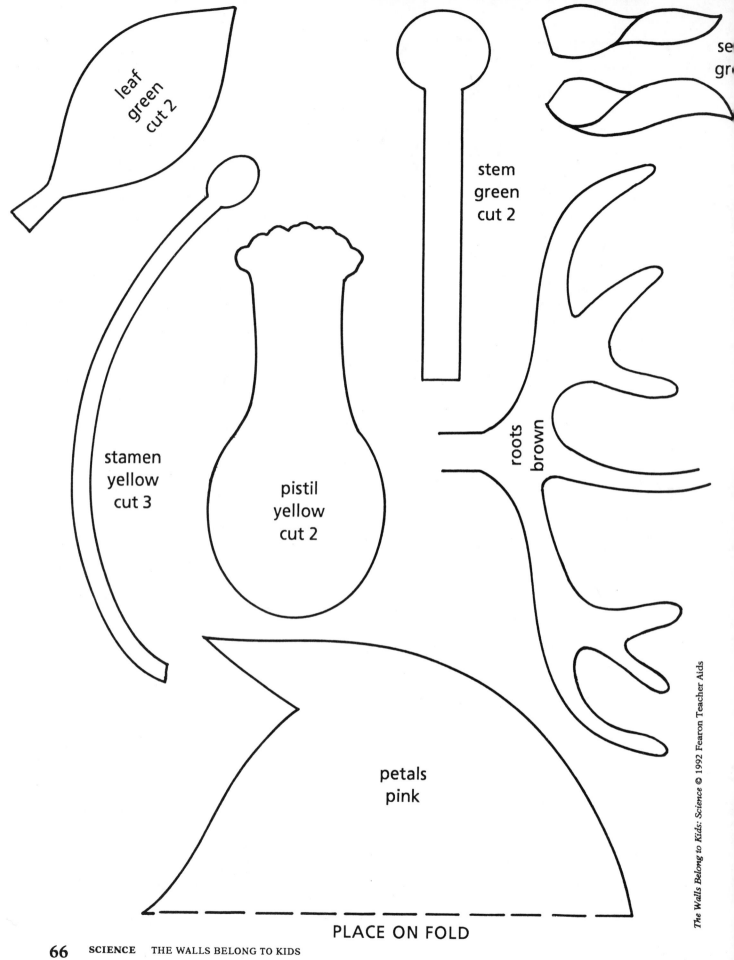

leaf
green
cut 2

stem
green
cut 2

se
gr

stamen
yellow
cut 3

pistil
yellow
cut 2

roots
brown

petals
pink

PLACE ON FOLD

The Walls Belong to Kids: Science © 1992 Fearon Teacher Aids

pistil	filament
pistil	sepal
stigma	receptacle
style	stem
ovary	stem
stamen	petals
stamen	roots
anther	leaves

Flower Matching Activity

Name _____

Look at the diagram of the flower. Write the letters of
the flower parts next to the appropriate names.

1. Leaves   _____

2. Roots   _____

3. Stem   _____

4. Petal   _____

5. Pistil   _____

6. Stamen   _____

7. Sepal   _____

8. Receptacle   _____

9. Ovary   _____

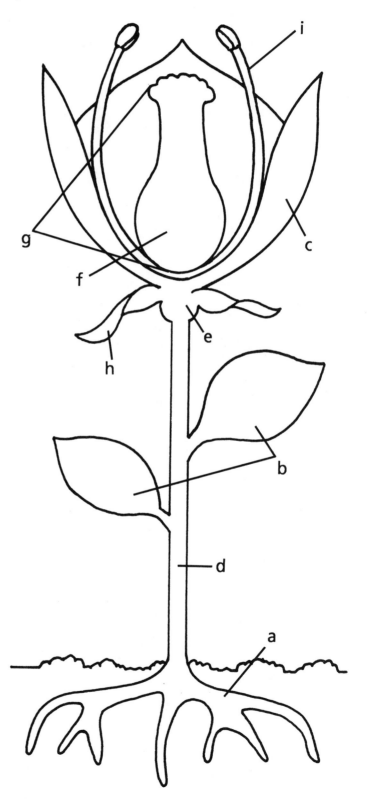

Flower Art Ideas

1. Cut out "V" shapes along the edge of a paper plate. Glue a construction-paper circle in the center.

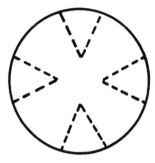 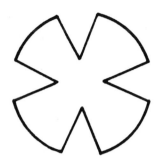 

2. Make slits in a paper cup. Push the sections down to form a flower.

3. Trace and cut out four hand shapes from sheets of construction paper. Glue the palms of the shapes together. Cut circles from different colors of construction paper to glue on the centers, as shown in the illustration below.

 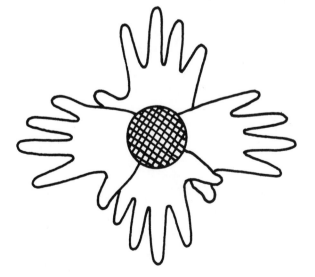

Name _____

Animal Recording Sheet

Animal's Name _____

Record facts about your animal. Draw a picture of your animal in the space provided.

Size _____

_____

Habitat _____

_____

Food Preferences _____

_____

Enemies _____

_____

Lizard Pattern

Name _____

My Planet Recording Sheet

My planet is _____.

How large is it? _____

_____

How far is it from the sun? _____

_____

Is it hot or cold? _____

Is there life on my planet? _____

If yes, what kind of life? _____

_____

What does the surface of my planet look like? _____

Draw a picture of your planet in the box below.

Star Patterns

Name _____

My Constellation's name is _____.

About My Constellation

_____

_____

_____

_____

_____

_____

_____

Draw a picture of your new constellation.

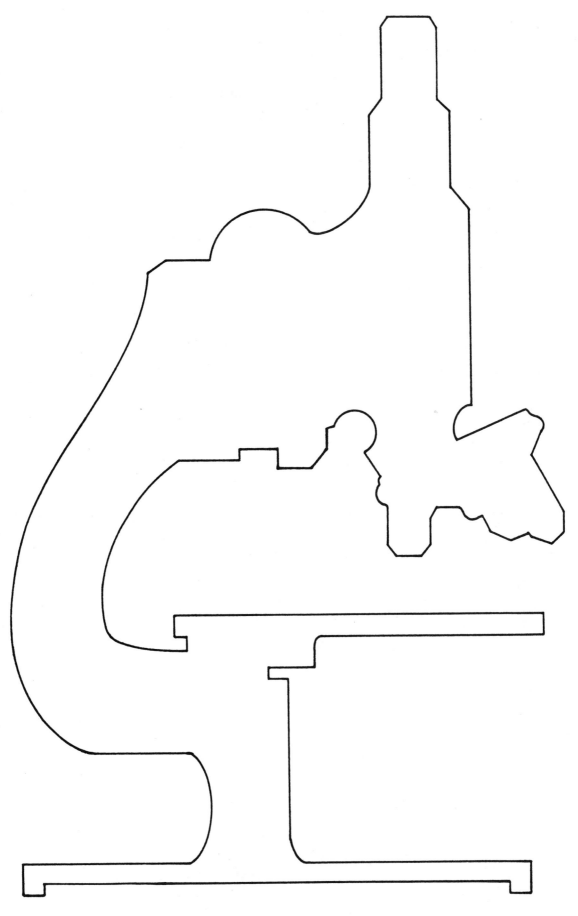

Name _____

My Observations Form

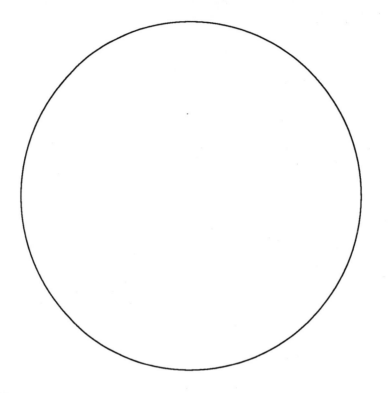

FOLD HERE

Our Observations

Names _____

_____

Butterfly Pattern

Cut out the butterfly pieces. Then glue the butterfly body to the wings on the shaded area. Color the body and wings different colors. Draw designs on the wings using crayons or felt pens, if you wish. Bend the wings so they fold away from the body.

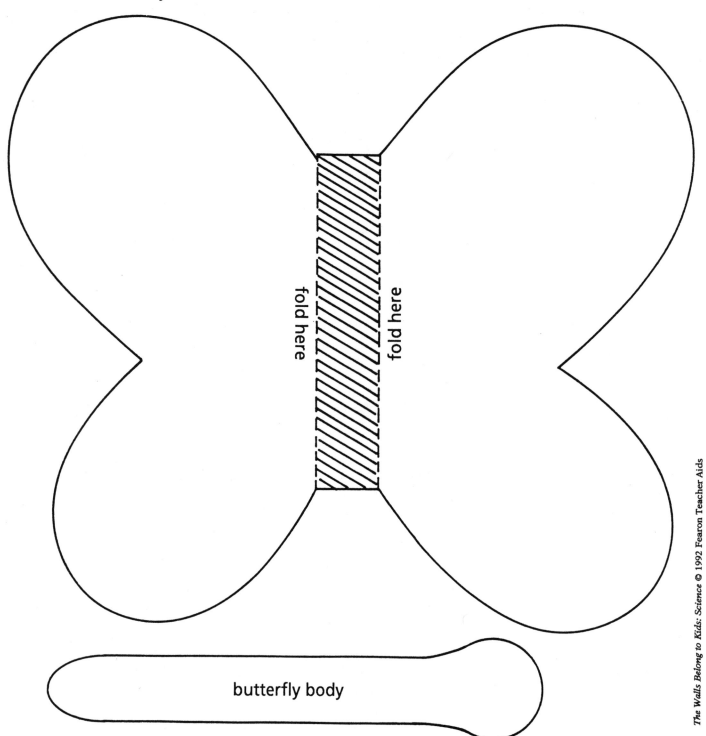

fold here

fold here

butterfly body

Tadpole Pattern

Trace and cut out the tadpole pattern from brown construction paper.

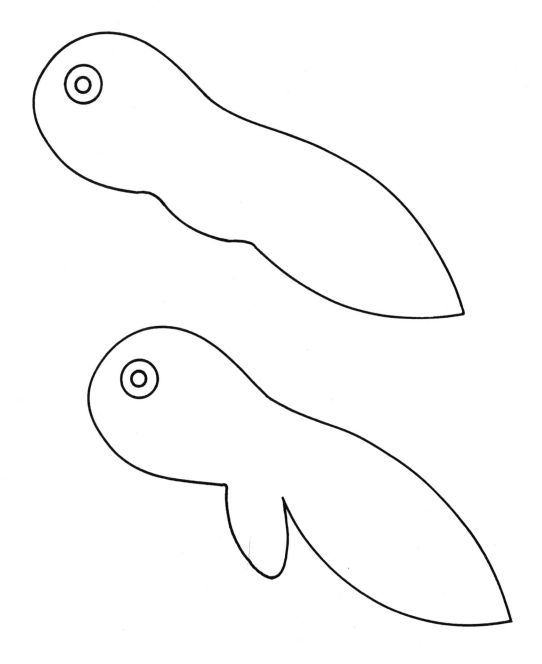

Frog Pattern

1. Fold a sheet of green construction paper in half. Place the frog leg pattern on the paper with the dotted line along the fold. Cut out the pattern.

2. Trace and cut out the head and eye patterns from green construction paper. Fold the eyes along the dotted lines. Then glue the eyes to the back of the frog's head. Glue the head to the frog legs.

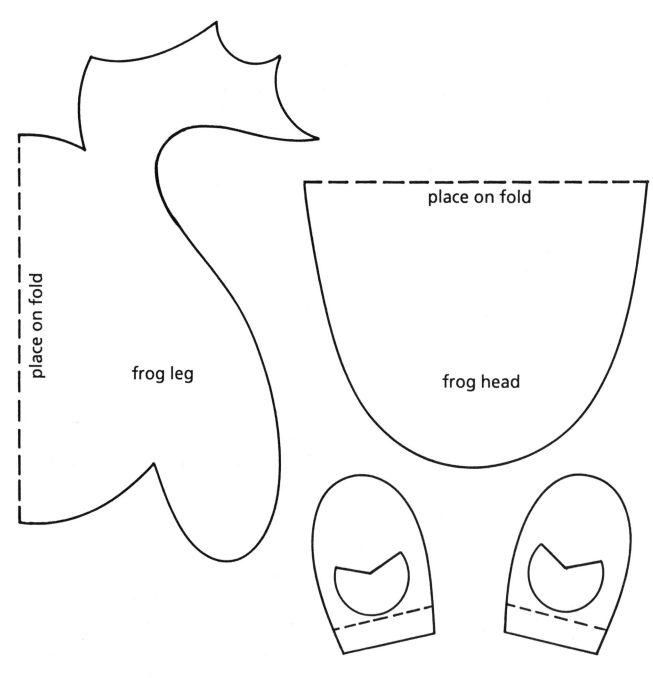

place on fold

frog leg

place on fold

frog head